LAST YEAR, when things were a little dull around the office and we were waiting around in between important publication dates, this publishing house issued a little book called *Pogo*. Several of the important officials in the office didn't understand why, and didn't even understand the book when they saw it. So, rather nervously, the book's proponents prepared a little one-column advertisement, hesitantly plunked up the few dollars necessary to run it, and waited.

They waited approximately 24 hours. A joyful shriek arose from Pogo fans throughout the nation who had been irritably clipping and pasting up the individual strips. Before the frantic telegrams from booksellers had been cleared away more than 200,000 people had rushed into bookstores and borne their copies fondly home.

Well, here's the new book about Pogo. It's no bigger than the last one, it's the same size. It's no better, it's just about the same sort of stuff. It contains the reasons why several hundred thousand *I Go Pogo* buttons are already being worn on undergraduate lapels throughout the country. The people who don't understand Pogo are fewer in number now, and hoarser. If you are one of them, you have been wasting your time reading this blurb.

I GO POGO

BY WALT KELLY

SIMON AND SCHUSTER • NEW YORK

PRINTED IN THE UNITED STATES OF AMERICA
BY WILLIAM KONECKY ASSOCIATES, INC., NEW YORK

"How Pierceful grows the Hazy Yon!
How Myrtle Petaled Thou!
For Spring hath Sprung the
Cyclotron,
How High Browse Thou, Brown Cow?"

Churchy Lafemme, 1950

CONTENTS

SLIGHTLY HOLIDAZED

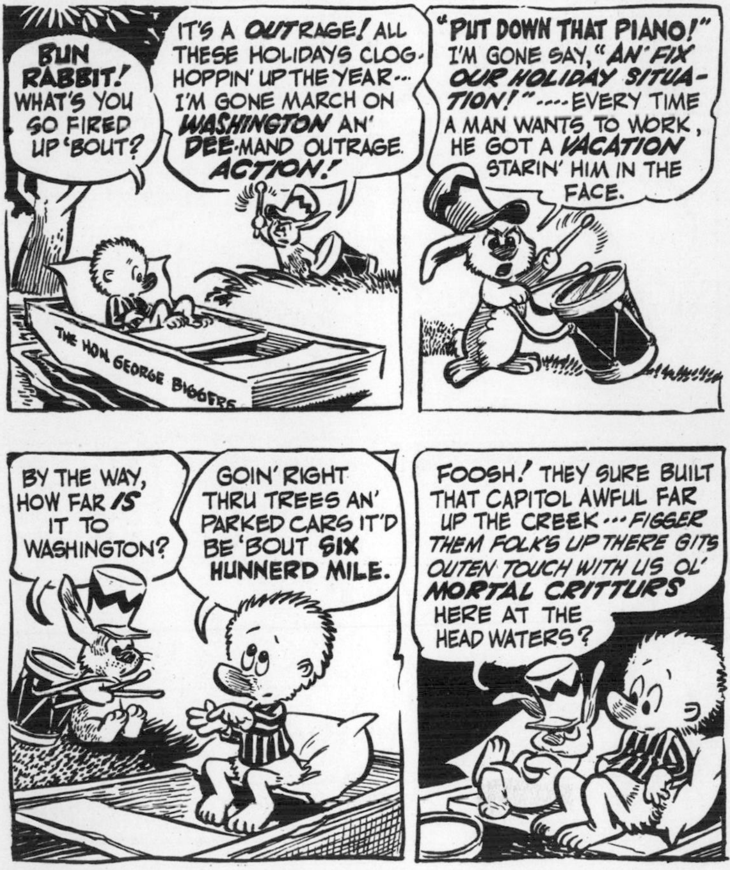

THE **MIDWINTER BEAR SOCIETY DANCE**; (HOLE UP SOME FINGERBONES) **THE DOWN UNDER CORROBORREE**; THE FESTA STULTORUM; THE DAY OF THE **KA**.

LAMMAS EVE; THE NIMAN KACHINA; UNCLE CHARLIE'S **ANNUAL** SHIVAREE; MARTINMAS; THE **FEAST** OF THE **HUNGRY GHOSTS**; KNIGHT RUPERT'S VISITING DAY......

SAVE ONE FOR MY BIRTHDAY... I ALLUS GIVES **THAT** A REAL **ROUSIN'**.

I HEAR TELL YOU FELLAS IS CELEBRATIN' **HOLIDAYS** FER FOLKS.

WELL, IN A WAY, YES... RIGHT NOW **BUN RABBIT** IS **CELEBRATIN'** THE **TAR** OUTEN **ABBOT'S BROMLEY ANTLER DANCE**.

FIGGER HE'D HAVE TIME TO OBSERVE **IGOR'S DAY** WITH A LI'L' DIGNIFIED SCREAMIN' AN' DRUMMIN'?

IGOR'S DAY? NEVER **HEERD** OF IT --- WE GOT ALL WE CAN HANDLE WITH **REGULATION** SOUTHERN **BONA** FRIED HOLIDAYS LIKE THE FEAST OF **GOIBNIU**!

WELL! LET'S GO, UNCLE **IGOR**! **STUFFY** IS AS **STUFFY** DO!

WHAT'S UNTIED? **WHITSUNTIDE**? WHAT'S UNTIED ON WHITSUNTIDE? **RAH**!

16

18

19

22

31

BLANKER VERSE WAS NE'ER BLUNK!

IN THAT CASE, *I WINS!* US MIGHT'S WELL ADMIT **MY** *142 PRE-TESTED POEMS* WRIT ON 142 PIECES OF PAPER WILL **OUT**WEIGH **YOUR ONE** PUNY POEM.

WELL, **HERE'S** WHAT **MINE** IS WRIT ON --- *OUTWEIGH THAT!*

I CAN'T READ MY 142 POEMS 'CAUSE ALBERT FLANG THAT OL' TOMBSTONE DOWN ATOP OF 'EM --- *I PROTEST* ---

NATURAL, IF WE CAN'T GIT THE STONE OFF'N THEM POEMS, WORM, **ALBERT** WILL WIN BY **DEFAULT.**

WHOOSH! SUDDENLY THIS STONE IS PICKED UP A LI'L WEIGHT--- *'BOUT A TON.*

ALBERT'S POEM ON THE STONE CAN'T WIN UNLESS **SOMEBODY** KNOWS WHAT IT MEANS.

FROM WHAT **I** KNOW 'BOUT POEMS, IT **CAN'T LOSE** IF **NOBODY** KNOWS WHAT IT MEANS.

"SI QUAERIS PENINSULAM AMOENAM, CIRCUMSPICE." .. *Hm, mebbe it means "The best part is underground."*

LOOKY HERE!

43

JUDGE SAY HE DON'T *WANT* NO UNDER-GROUND SUBVERSIVE POEMS.

WIPS GRIMMIS GOBF WM?

HERE'S ONE OF MINE WHAT IS LEFT!

Wretched Richard, richened sweet, By the fingers of his feet, Toted tuppence with his toes, Nodding nimbly next his nose... The mist must myrtle on the way While minst..

HEY! YOU *HEERD* THE RULING IN THE LAST PANEL!

ALBERT, US MOUGHT AS WELL *ADMIT* YOU DIN'T WRITE *NO* POETRY WORTH READIN' --- *SO* US GOTTA AWARD THE PRIZE TO THE *WORM.*

Oh, *NO*, YOU DON'T.! *MR. WORM* IS BEEN SWIPIN' *ALL* OF LI'L' *BERNICE ELEANOR'S HOME WORK* IN THE ENGLISH CLASS! LI'L' BERNICE ELEANOR IS *RESPONSIBOBBLE* FOR THEM POETRIES.

HAW! COULDN'T EVEN RHYME AGIN A *CHILE!*

AW, *SHE* BUN TO *KIDNEYGARTEN.*

WELL, THE PRIZE GOES TO *BERNICE.* WHAT HAPPENED TO THAT WRAPPED BOOK OF *EDGAR A. GUEST'S POEMS?*

WOWP! *THAT* WAS *POEMS?* IT WAS *SO* PERTY, I *THUNK* IT WERE A *CAKE* ------ ME AN' OWL *ET* IT!

ANY GOOD?

NEMMINE, BERNICE HONEY, US'LL GO HOME AN' HAVE A BIRTHDAY.

IT IS HARD TO KEEP A HEAD

46

49

51

57

60

71

THE TIGER GOIN' OFF TO LOOK FOR FOOD REMINDS ME OF A TIME WE WAS FORAGIN' FOR GRUB DURIN' THE BOXER REBELLION ----

ME AN' ANOTHER MEMBER OF THE CAVALRY, A FELLOW WHO WAS A HORSE AT THE TIME, CAME UPON A FINE FAT ELEPHANT WHICH WAS JUST *WAITIN'* TO BE *EATEN* --- *WELL, SIR*, WE QUIETLY CARVED IT INTO STEAKS IN MY TENT ONE NIGHT BETWEEN VESPERS AN' TAPS.

WHEN MY COMPANION RECALLED HE WAS A *VEGETARIAN* ... *RATHER'N HAVE HIM* BREAK HIS *VOWS*, I HAD TO EAT THE *WHOLE* WORKS ... I'M FINISHIN', SEE, WHEN IN COMES THE SARGE ... *"YOU CHAPS SEEN OUR NEW COMMANDER?"* HE ASKS ----

"FELLOW IN A GREY SUIT.. GOT A FIERCE LONG TRUNK ON HIM!" ... WELL, YOU CAN IMAGINE HOW I FELT ... *TAR TAKE THEM KINGFISHERS!* THEY'RE THICKER'N SWAMP-WATER COFFEE.

WHY, *HEY, THERE*, OL' PIGEON! THOUGHT YOU WAS IN WASHINGTON. *DID YOU SEE A KINGFISHER WHAT STOLE A FISH FROM MY FRIEND, THE MOUSE?*

HELLO, SON! NO, NOT NOW. MAYBE I *DID*. DID HE INDEED?

I'M TEACHIN' YOUNG FOLKS TO FLY AN' IT SEEM LIKE I *DO* GOT A KINGFISHER TAD IN THE CLASS .. *HEY, AL! AL!*

The SAFER SAFARI

89

'CAUSE US IS NEW-BORNED FOREIGN TYPE OF REFUGEES AN' GOT NO UNCLE SAM.

YOU CONVINCES ME! WHAT LANGUAGE IS YOU SPEAKIN'? SEEM LIKE I UNDERSTAN'S HER PERTY GOOD.

TOVARISCH! WHAT YOU KNOW?! WE IS RUNNED ACROSS A SLEIGHFUL OF OUR COUNTRY-MEN! THEY TALKS LATIN, TOO!

LET'S ALL ROOM TOGETHER NEXT TERM.

CAVE CANEM

WHO ALL IS LOOKIN' FOR THE RACKETY-COON CHILE AN' THE PUP-DOG, UNCLE POGO? I MEAN STRANGER.

WELL, STRANGER, EVER'BODY INCLUDIN' YO' PAP...I MEAN MR. RACKETY-COON...AN' US IS SPREAD PERTY THIN, STRANGER.

A FEW IS HUNTIN' IN THE HOLLER.. MORE IS STOMPIN' 'ROUND BOWLEG'S ISLAND... BOATS IS PLYIN' THE DARK WATERS

NOT 'NUFF MEN TO SAIL 'EM-- SO EACH GOT A SKELETON CREW.

A SKELETON CREW?

SKELETON

WHOO! I IS FOUND NOW! CALL OFF THEM BONEYARD BIRDS!

I DECLARE! I IS NEVER BEEN MORE SURPRISED!

NEITHER IS ME!

91

94

WHIRLED SERIES

103

105

106

109

Finally we have a cryptic bit written by Turtle that *reeks* of guilt.

"SMILE, WAVERING WINGS, ABOVE RAINS POUR, WHILE HOPEFULLY SINGS LOVE OF SHORN SHORE. SHORE SHORN OF LOVE SINGS HOPEFULLY WHILE, POUR RAINS ABOVE, WINGS WAVERING, SMILE."

I DON'T GIT IT.

THAT'S THE *CLEVER PART.* IT'S GOTTA BE READ *BACKWARD.*

YEP! IT GOES FROM *RIGHT* TO *LEFT.*

"Here it is backward: *Smile, wavering wings, Above rains pour, While hopefully sings Love of shorn shore. Shore shorn of Love Sings hopefully while pour rains above Wings wavering smile.*"

THERE!

YOU KNOW, IF I DIN'T *HEAR* YOU READ THAT, I WOULDN'T *BELIEVE MY EARS!*

WELL, IT LOOKS LIKE THE *EVIDENCE* IS PILED UP AGIN TURTLE...

ONLY THING EVIDENT SO FAR IS THE FOX, CAT AN' BUZZARD WANTS HIM IN THE *SOUP.*

BUT YOU *SAW* THE SPY *BOOK!*

FULL OF BLANK PAPER!

114

117

118

AND, AFTER 16 HOURS OF PRACTICING

136

139

146

148

149

154

ABANDON IT THEN---ONCE A PARTY IS **NESTED**, *NEVER DISTURB IT*--- I MIND ONE TIME ME AN' **LUCKY JACK LARKIN** BUILT US A NEST OF SCRAPS IN THE DERBY OF A EMINENT BANK PRES. ---*WELL*, *SIR*-- WE JUST GOT--

A FAVORABLE GAME GOIN' WHEN THE PREXY GRABS HIS LID AN' GOES TO LUNCH. WE WAS ALL HAULED IN FOR ABSCONDIMENT----SEEMS WE'D TORE UP LARGE BILLS FOR THE NEST -- THE PRES WAS A GOOD MAN TO BE IN THE POKEY WITH-- HE-- *HEY!*

TAMMANANNY, A *GROSS BLOW* has befallen POGO'S CANDIDATURE

HE'S MADE A SPEECH?

NO, he was mixed up with some *COWBIRDS!* The Deacon claims it *Blackens* POGO'S name

SOMEONE MUST ENDORSE POGO'S CHARACTER!

YES! It will take a man of **PROVEN** *MERIT!* A CITIZEN WHO *TOWERS* ABOVE THE CROWD. ★★ A FIGURE ADMIRED *and* BELOVED by *ALL !!!*

IT'LL BE HARD TO GET SUCH A MAN TO SPEAK UP AND RISK HIS *OWN* GOOD NAME.

SAY NOT *SO!!* These are TIMES for **STALWARCY** & **PLUCK** One noble soul must risk it I, P.T. BRIDGEPORT *WILL SPEAK FOR POGO!!*

YOU SURE THAT FIGURE IS *UNIVERSALLY ADMIRED?*

165

RIGHT ON THE BUTTON

LEFT AT THE POST

184

188

189

190